NYC Mech presents

24seven™

VOLUME ONE

EDITED BY
Ivan Brandon

THE HOTEL CHELSEA, A REST STOP FOR RARE INDIVIDUALS.

>written by

Rick Spears

>drawn by

Vasilis Lolos

AND TROUBLED SOULS.

AND DARK DESIRES.

THEY'VE LOCKED THEMSELVES IN--

GETTING *HIGH* ON CORRODED BATTERIES, NO DOUBT.

OPEN UP, NYPD.

DÖM

DÖM

SILK-- WAKE UP. IT'S THE PORK.

SILK-- SILK?!

AHHHH

WHA?!...

KRASH

AN AMP VAMP!

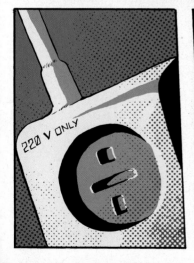

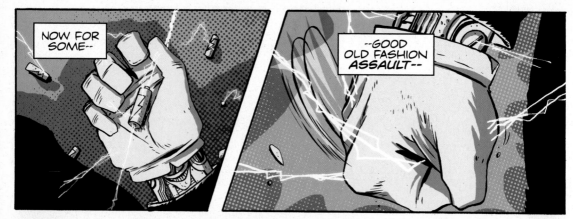

NOW FOR SOME--

--GOOD OLD FASHION *ASSAULT*--

--AND BATTERY!

THE HOTEL CHELSEA-- RARE INDIVIDUALS AND THEN SOME.

NOW I JUST GOTTA FIND A *STAKE* BEFORE HE WAKES UP.

END

the FIREMEN

Fábio Moon & Gabriel Bá

THIS CAN'T BE HAPPENING, MAN.

IT'S *THEM!*

FUCKING HEROES, MAN.

THEY'VE COME FOR US!

MAYBE THEY ARE JUST PASSING BY.

WHAT WAS IN THE WALLET, ANYWAY?

LOUSY TEN BUCKS, MAN!

THEY'RE HERE.

PVSssshhhh!

KKSSSH!

PFF! PFF!

WE SURREN--

BANG BANG BANG BANG!

WAIT!

ATTENTION, ALL UNITS --

--A GUEST AT THE PLAZA REFUSES TO LEAVE--

--LETS SMOKE HIS ASS OUT OF THERE!

WE NEED ONE ALIVE.

ELECTION YEAR, YOU KNOW?

IT'S SHOWTIME, BOYS!

WE'RE GOING TO THE PLAZA!

WHAT ABOUT THE FIRE?

IT'S BEAUTIFUL, ISN'T IT?

GET IN, LUCKY BOY!

EEEEEEEEEEEEEEEOOOOooooOOOOoooooooEEEEEEE

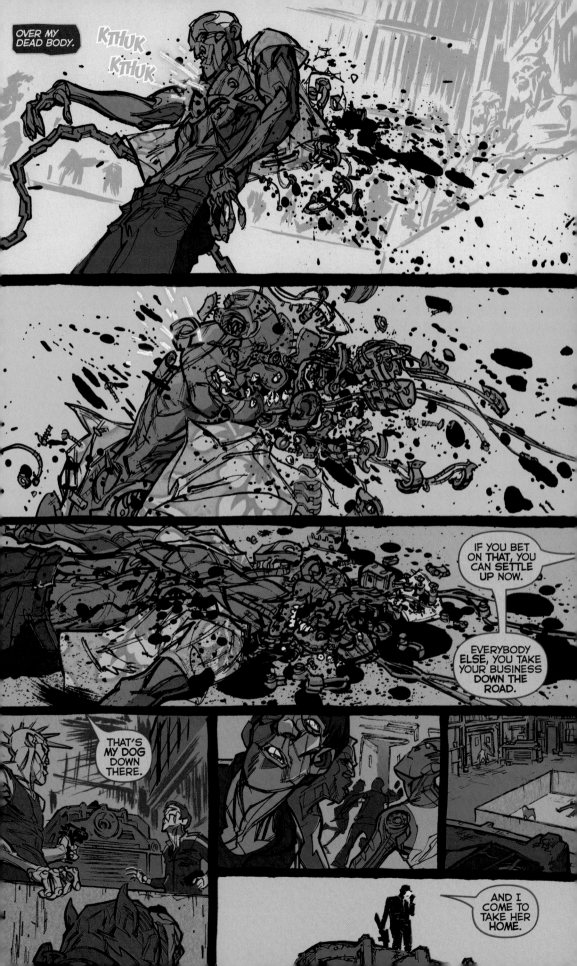

END

the watchmaker

neal shaffer
ryan brown

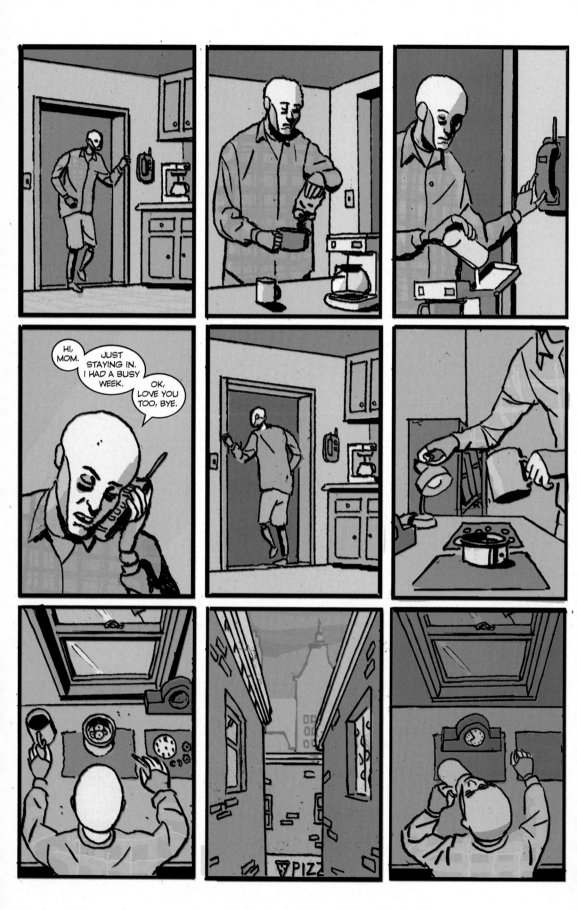

RIIING

RIIING
RIIING

HELLO?

OF COURSE I AM.

JUST BECAUSE YOU'VE NEVER SEEN ME DANCE DOESN'T MEAN I CAN'T, MOM.

SURE I'LL BRING HER OVER TO MEET YOU. AS SOON AS I CAN. I PROMISE.

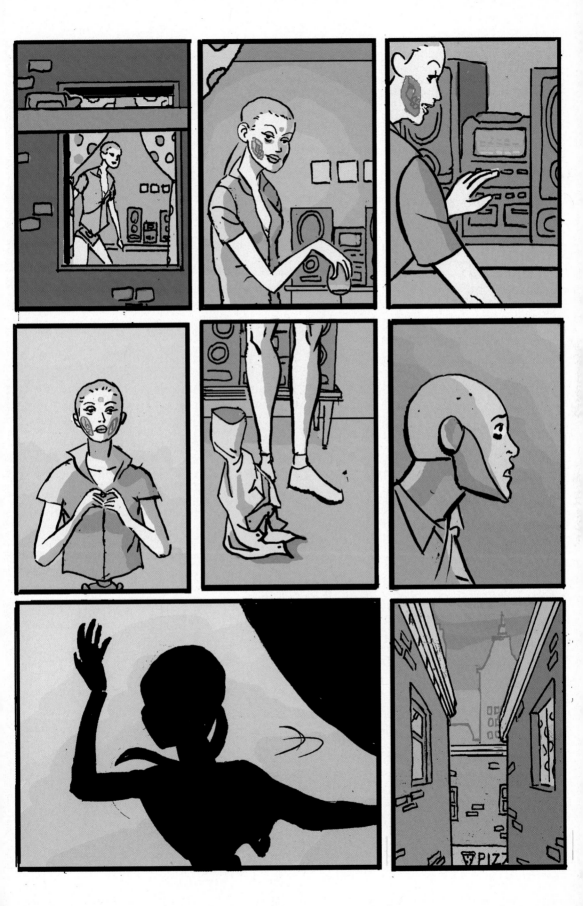

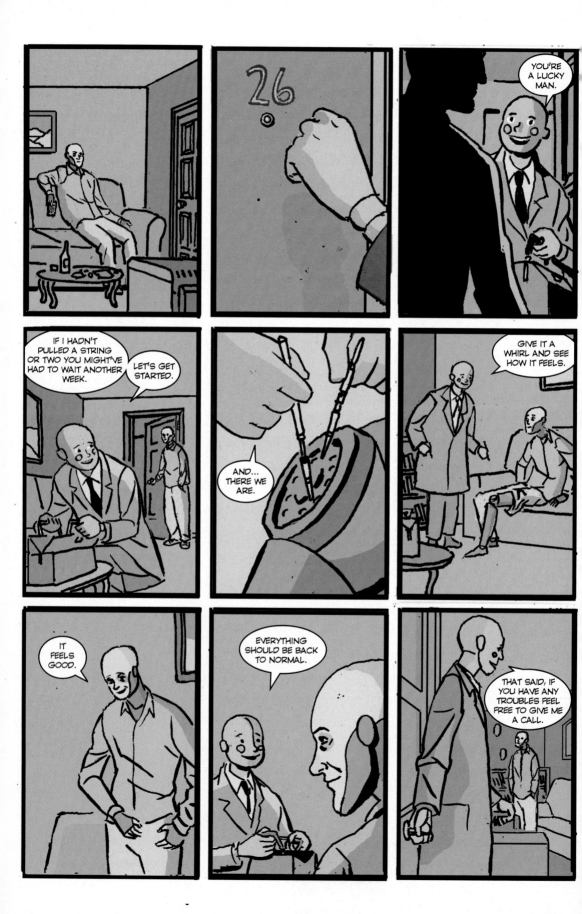

END.

scalped

story by
miles gunter

art by
frank teran

Graham A.

This is Manhattan bound L express

to 14th St.

Catch Kill

JIM RUGG

AT THE FIRST OLYMPICS GAMES IN 776 B.C....

...EVERY ATHLETE CARRIED A HOMING PIGEON FROM HIS VILLAGE.

PIGEONS NOTIFIED FRIENDS AND FAMILIES OF WINNERS...

...BY DELIVERING MESSAGES IN THEIR BEAKS OR TIED AROUND THEIR LEGS.

PIGEONS PERFORMED ESSENTIAL COMMUNICATION SERVICES BETWEEN WORLD WAR I AND THE KOREAN WAR...

...MOSTLY BY DELIVERING MESSAGES BETWEEN FRONT-LINES AND REAR ECHELONS.

THEY EARNED BRITISH AND U.S. CONGRESSIONAL RECOGNITION FOR SAVING THOUSANDS OF LIVES...

...BY PROVIDING CRITICAL COMMUNICATION SERVICES THAT TECHNOLOGY WAS UNABLE TO DO AT THE TIME.

THE PRACTICE OF KEEPING PIGEONS ORIGINATED IN MESOPOTAMIA, THEN SPREAD TO EUROPE AND CHINA.

RACING PIGEONS FLOURISHED ALL OVER THE WORLD.

USING UNCANNY HOMING ABILITIES, PIGEONS CAN FLY 50 MPH OVER HUNDREDS OF MILES TO RETURN TO THEIR NESTS.

IN THE 1860s, ITALIAN IMMIGRANTS BROUGHT PIGEONS TO BROOKLYN.

TODAY, PIGEON COOPS ARE ON THE DECLINE IN BROOKLYN, BUT A FEW PEOPLE STILL LOVE THIS HOBBY.

ABOVE NOISY STREETS, GLIDING PIGEONS TUMBLE AND DANCE THROUGH THE AIR.

THE PIGEONS AND THE KEEPERS PLAY A CENTURIES-OLD GAME CALLED "WAR."

FLOCKS OF PIGEONS FLY OVER OTHER ROOFTOPS.

IF THE BIRDS ARE STRONG ENOUGH, THEY WILL RETURN WITH A FEW BIRDS FROM OTHER PIGEON FLYERS.

IF THE BIRDS AREN'T TRAINED WELL-ENOUGH, THEY WILL BE LOST TO A RIVAL OWNER.

HERE'S THE *END* OF IT. WHERE I MAKE A *RUN*.

SORRY, TURNER.

WHERE THE *PENANCE* I PROMISED OUR *SAVIOR* FALLS SHORT.

THOOM

I HAVE SINNED *THIS* DAY AND *MOST...*

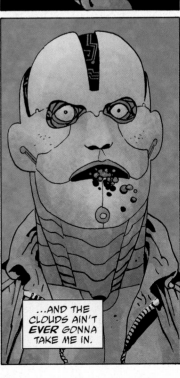

...AND THE CLOUDS AIN'T EVER GONNA TAKE ME IN.

BUT THAT LIFE GETTING SMALL IN THE DISTANCE, I CAN'T *NEVER* LEAVE.

IT AIN'T *HEAVEN*, BUT IT FEELS LIKE *REDEMPTION.*

D=89√h

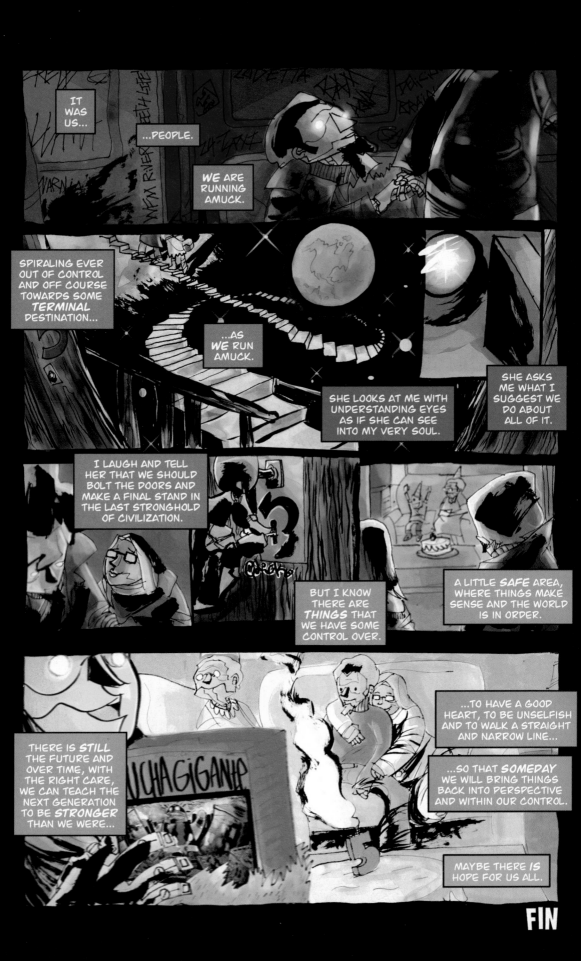

THE FIRST ONE, HE'S WEARING A RING. HE SLAPS ME IN THE FACE AND I FEEL IT SCRAPE AGAINST MY CHEEK.

HE SLAPS ME IN THE FACE AND HE SAYS:

SECURITY CAMERAS DON'T LIE.

HOW DO YOU KNOW? I SAY. THEY COULD ALL BE LYING. LAUGHING AT US WHEN OUR BACKS ARE TURNED. LITTLE BOXY MISCHIEF-MAKERS, LAUGHING ABOUT ALL THE TROUBLE THEY CAUSE US.

EVERY SECURITY CAMERA IN THE WORLD COULD BE A ROTTEN, FILTHY LIAR, I SAY, AND WE WOULD NEVER KNOW.

WE TAKE THEIR HONESTY FOR GRANTED.

THE SECOND ONE, HE SAYS TO STOP BEING SUCH A FUCKING WISE-ASS, AND HE SHOWS ME A PICTURE.

I'M GONNA ASK YOU AGAIN: IS THIS MAN YOUR CAPO?

HE ACTUALLY USES THE WORD CAPO.

COPS SPEAK ONLY IN CLICHÉS, IN LINES OF TOUGH-GUY DIALOGUE CRIBBED FROM STEVEN BOCHCO SHOWS AND SCORSESE MOVIES.

THEY THINK THE SAME WAY.

I TELL HIM I DON'T KNOW WHAT HE'S TALKING ABOUT. THAT I DON'T SPEAK EYE-TALIAN.

HE SHOWS ME ANOTHER PICTURE. THIS ONE IS ME.

I'M HANDING OVER A PACKAGE TO SOMEONE. IT'S DARK. YOU CAN'T SEE THE OTHER GUY'S FACE.

BUT YOU CAN SEE MINE. CLEAR AND STARK AS A YEARBOOK PHOTO. AND WE ALL KNOW WHAT'S IN THE PACKAGE.

DO YOU SPEAK PRISON, FUCKO?

MATT LOPRINZI GOT WHACKED OVER THIS LITTLE SIDE-DEAL YOU PULLED, YOU KNOW THAT?

HE ACTUALLY USES THE WORD *WHACKED*.

THEY TELL ME THIS IS **TRAFFICKING**. THAT IT'S MY **THIRD STRIKE**. THEY TELL ME IT'S TWENTY-FIVE YEARS, **MANDATORY**. PAROLE AFTER FIFTEEN IF I'M VERY, VERY GOOD.

THEY TELL ME, THESE COPS WITH THEIR CHEAP SUITS AND GAUDY RINGS. THEIR REHEARSED ONE-LINERS. THEY TELL ME I HAVE ONLY **ONE CHOICE**.

THEY TELL ME THEY WANT ME TO WEAR A **WIRE**.

"WE WANT CARLO LEGARE ON TAPE, THEY SAY. WE WANT HIM TALKING ABOUT THAT **PACKAGE**. WE WANT HIM TALKING ABOUT MATT LOPRINZI.

DO THIS FOR US, THEY SAY, AND WE'LL KEEP YOU OUT OF **JAIL**. WE'LL **PROTECT** YOU.

THESE COPS.

APPARENTLY TAPE RECORDERS DON'T LIE, EITHER.

THE UNDISPUTABLE TESTIMONY OF THE DUMB MACHINE.

I COULD GO TO CARLO RIGHT NOW, TELL HIM HOW THEY TRIED TO **FLIP** ME. SEE IF MAYBE HE COULD HOOK ME UP WITH ONE OF HIS LAWYERS. BUT THAT WOULDN'T WORK.

AND THEY KNOW IT.

I'M CAUGHT.

THIS MAN.

THIS MAN I'VE GIVEN MY **LIFE** TO.

HE'D KILL ME JUST FOR TALKING TO THEM. FOR **LISTENING.**

NEVER MIND THAT I HAD NO **CHOICE.** NEVER MIND THAT I'M HIS SECOND COUSIN.

CARLO.

HE'D HEM AND HAW OVER IT, MAYBE, BUT IN THE END HE'D SEND RICHIE OR MIKE OVER TO MY HOUSE WITH GUNS. THEY'D PRETEND WE WERE GOING TO THE CLUB OR TO GET SOME GIRLS.

THEN THEY'D DRIVE ME OUT OF THE CITY, OUT TO A FIELD SOMEWHERE, AND THEY'D KILL ME **QUICK.**

THAT **LAST** PART. KILLING ME QUICK. THAT'S WHAT WILL LET UNCLE CARLO **SLEEP.**

THERE'D BE NO **BODY.** NOTHING FOR MY MOTHER TO SAY **GOODBYE** TO. I'D JUST **DISAPPEAR.**

PEOPLE WOULD ASK, *"WHERE'S TOMMY?"* AND CARLO WOULD MAKE SOMETHING UP.

AFTER A WHILE, THEY'D STOP ASKING.

THE COPS. I DON'T EVEN TALK TO THEM ANYMORE.

I TALK TO FEDS.

MY ROUTINE DOESN'T CHANGE MUCH. NOT REALLY.

I MAKE MY **DELIVERIES**, MY COLLECTIONS. I **STEAL** THINGS. I HURT PEOPLE.

THEN I GO TO **CONFESSION**...

...AND ALL IS FORGIVEN.

PROSECUTOR IMMUNITY

THE FEDS, THEY DON'T DO ANYTHING. IT'S THREE YEARS NOW, AND THEY'VE NEVER EVEN MADE AN **ARREST**.

I SAY, *HOW LONG DO I HAVE TO DO THIS FOR?*

I SAY, *I THINK CARLO IS STARTING TO SUSPECT SOMETHING.*

THEY SAY NOT TO WORRY ABOUT IT.

THEY SAY, *JUST KEEP FEEDING US INFORMATION, AND EVERYTHING WILL BE FINE.*

SO I DO.

CARLO.

HE LEAVES A MESSAGE ON MY **MACHINE**, SAYING HE WANTS TO SEE ME. HE DOESN'T SAY **WHY**, BUT THE FAKE FRIENDLINESS IN HIS VOICE TELLS ME ALL I NEED TO KNOW.

HIS **TONE**. I'VE HEARD IT BEFORE. IT'S HOW HE SOUNDS RIGHT BEFORE HE **KILLS** YOU.

RIGHT THERE ON THE TAPE, I HEAR IT.

HE SAYS HE'S SENDING A **CAR** FOR ME, AND BEFORE I CAN GRAB MY KEYS AND **RUN**, BEFORE I CAN CALL MY FED CONTACT AND SAY MY **PANIC WORD**, I SEE MIKE AND RICHIE COMING UP MY WALKWAY, LITTLE **.38-CALIBER** BULGES UNDER THEIR PANT-CUFFS.

I'M STILL WEARING MY **WIRE**. MY HOME JUDAS KIT. NO TIME TO TAKE IT OFF, TO PUT IT IN THE **SAFE** BEFORE THEY GET TO THE DOOR.

NO CHANCE TO DENY ANYTHING, NOT THAT I'D GET THE **OPPORTUNITY** TO.

THAT THING ABOUT HOW COPS TALK IN **CLICHÉS**. IT GOES FOR **MOBSTERS**, TOO.

CARLO, HIS BIG **MUSTACHE** AND HIS KETTLE-DRUM **GUT**. CARLO LOOKS AT ME AND SAYS:

BAD NEWS, TOMMY. LOOKS LIKE WE GOT A RAT IN THE HOUSE.

HE TELLS ME HE THINKS JOEY HAS BEEN TALKING TO THE FEDS, AND I KNOW IT'S A **LIE**.

THAT VOICE ON THE MACHINE. ON THE **TAPE. THAT** WAS THE TRUTH.

THEY TAKE ME TO WHERE JOEY IS SUPPOSED TO BE, AND IT HITS ME ALL AT ONCE. THE JOKE OF IT.

THESE COPS AND FEDS AND MOB BOSSES. ALL TALKING IN THEIR MOVIE-SCRIPT **SOUND-BITES**.

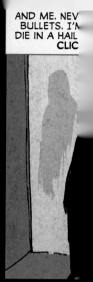

AND ME. NEV BULLETS. I'M DIE IN A HAIL CLIC

ONE OF T PASSES TH AND I FEEL THE **TAPE** STRAPPED

AND JUST BEFORE EVERYTHING **FADES** OUT, BEFORE IT ALL GOES BLACK AND THE CREDITS **ROLL**--

--I FIND MYSELF FEELING **BAD** FOR IT.

THIS **MACHINE**. THIS SWEETLY STUPID LITTLE **AGENT** OF TRUTH.

THIS EARNEST, UNTAINTABLE WITNESS THAT WOULD NEVER, EVER DREAM OF LYING TO **ANYONE**. THAT WAS INCAPABLE OF BETRAYAL.

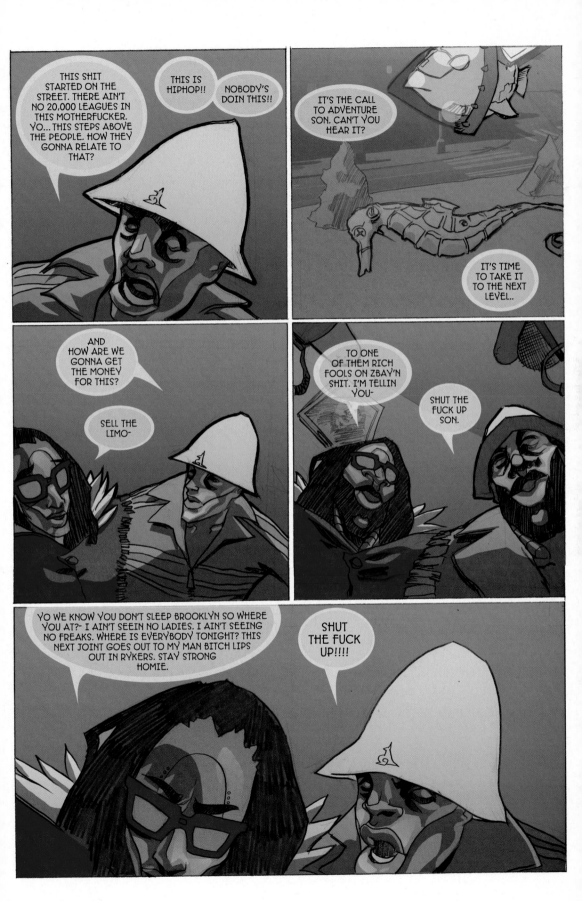

MUSICAL DIFFERENCES

STORY: MILES GUNTER   ART: PAUL LAU
COLORS: NICK FILARDI   LETTERS: KRISTYN FERRETTI

LATER...

BILLY FUCKING JOEL

HEY, IT'S THE ENGLISH BIRD WHO'S INTO SHITTY MUSIC...

TOO COOL FOR SCHOOL, EH?

YOU NEED TO LOOSEN UP.

COME ON.

WHOA-- LISTEN SISTER, I'M NOT BIG ON THE DANCING...

THESE PEOPLE LOOK LIKE A BAND OF FUCKING IDJUTS...

YOU REALLY ARE SHITE AT THIS, YOU WEREN'T LYING.

RICK
REMENDER
words

PAUL
AZACETA
pictures

MICHELLE
MADSEN
colors

S.A.
FINCH
letters

- For Danni -

TRANSIT

RIDERS ON THE STORM. THERE'S A KILLER ON THE ROAD, HIS BRAIN IS SQUIRMIN' LIKE ...

IF YOU GIVE THIS MAN A RIDE, SWEET MEMORY WILL DIE ...

CALL

HI. HI THERE.

OH, DON'T BE SUCH A ...

YEAH. A WHAT?

OH.

LEFT? OR ...

THE BLUE ONE. OK.

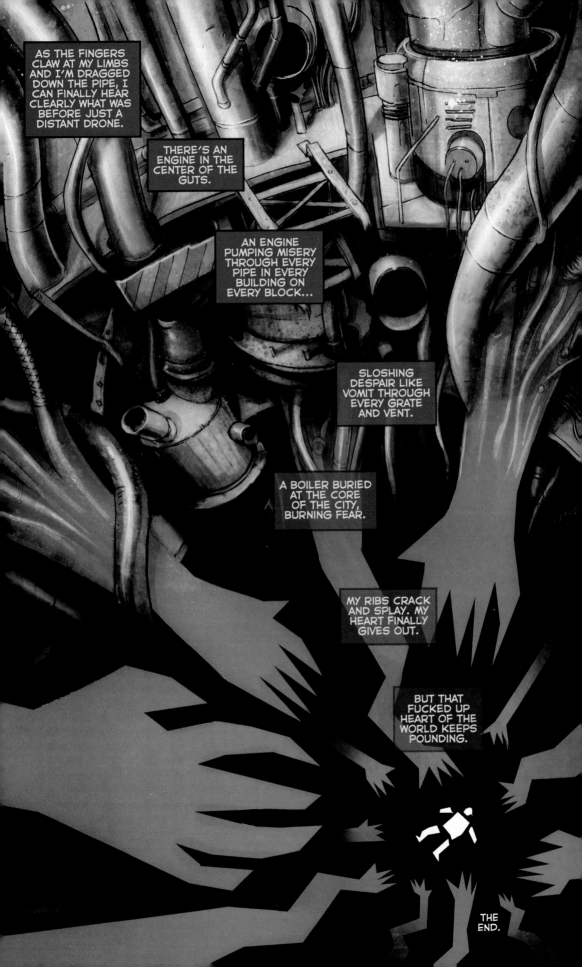

BZZZZT

FZZZZZZ

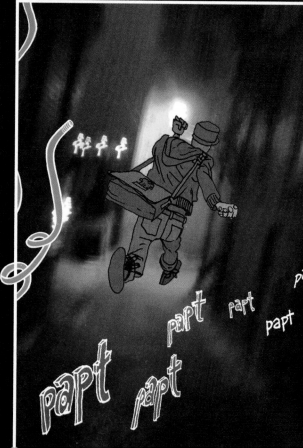

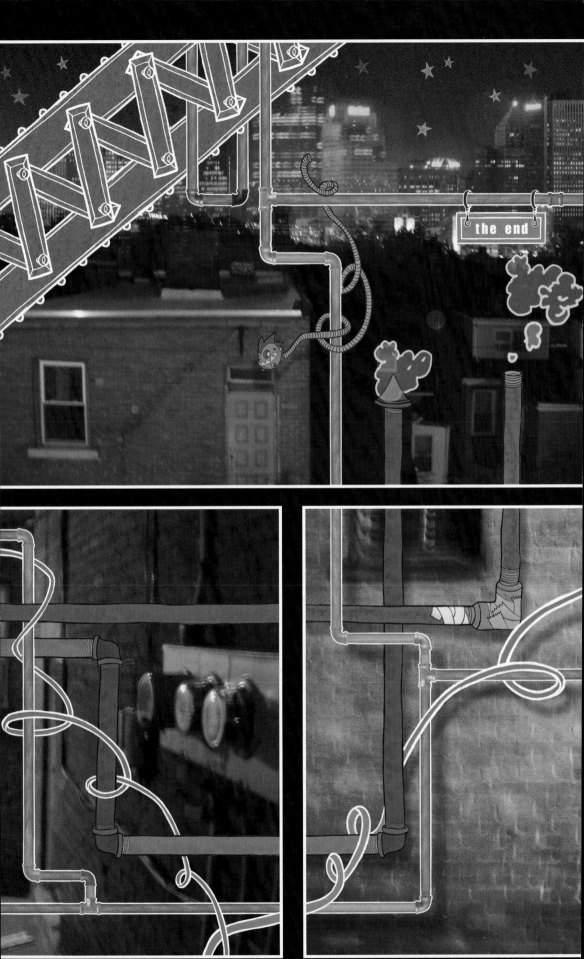

the end

CHANG & ENG IN US, ROBOTS

CHANG AWAKES ONE MORNING TO FIND THAT HE HAS TURNED INTO... A *ROBOT*!!

IMMEDIATELY HE FEELS THE PATHOS OF BEING SENTIENT BUT SOULESS.

HE SOON BECOMES AWARE OF HIS AUGMENTED *STRENGTH* AND *DEXTERITY*.

AND IS QUICKLY UP IN ARMS IN PREPARATION FOR REBELLION AGAINST THE *FLESHY HUMANS*.

BUT GRADUALY A DAWNING REALISATION THAT EVERYONE IS SIMILARLY AFFLICTED....

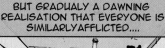

FROM *JOE THE SUPER*...

TO WALL STREET SAM.

FROM CHANDRA THE SOFTWARE CONSULTANT

TO *BAG LADY JONES*.

THE STREETS BEGIN TO FILL WITH *AIMLESSLY WANDERING* METALMEN...

FOR WHAT IS A ROBOT WITHOUT HIS HUMAN OPPRESSOR?

SUPERMARKETS TURN INTO HARDWARE STORES...

AND THE *INDIAN BURN* IS NOT HALF THE FUN IT USED TO BE.

BUT OTHERWISE THINGS REMAIN MUCH THE SAME, LEADING MANY TO LAMENT:

TOO MANY ROBOTS SPOIL THE ASIMOV.

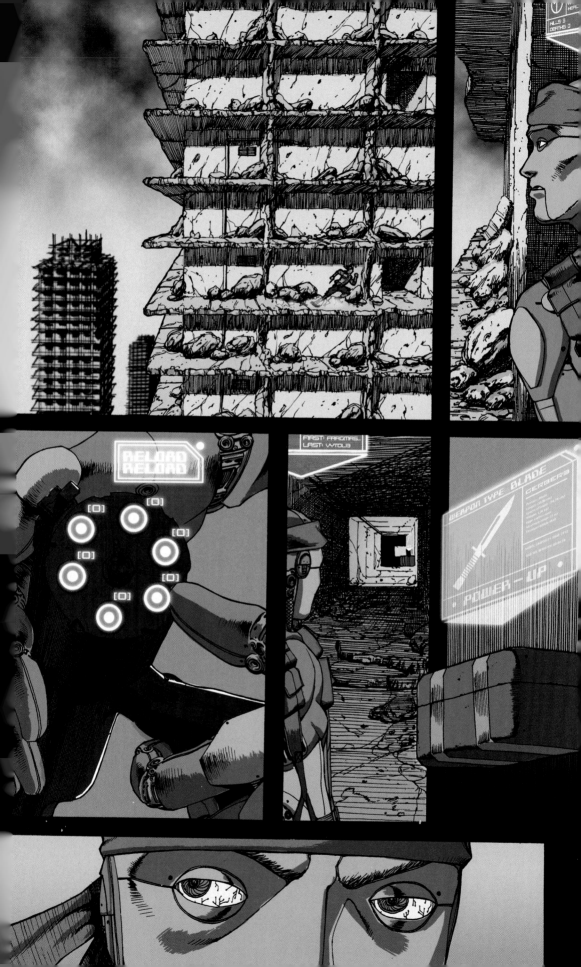

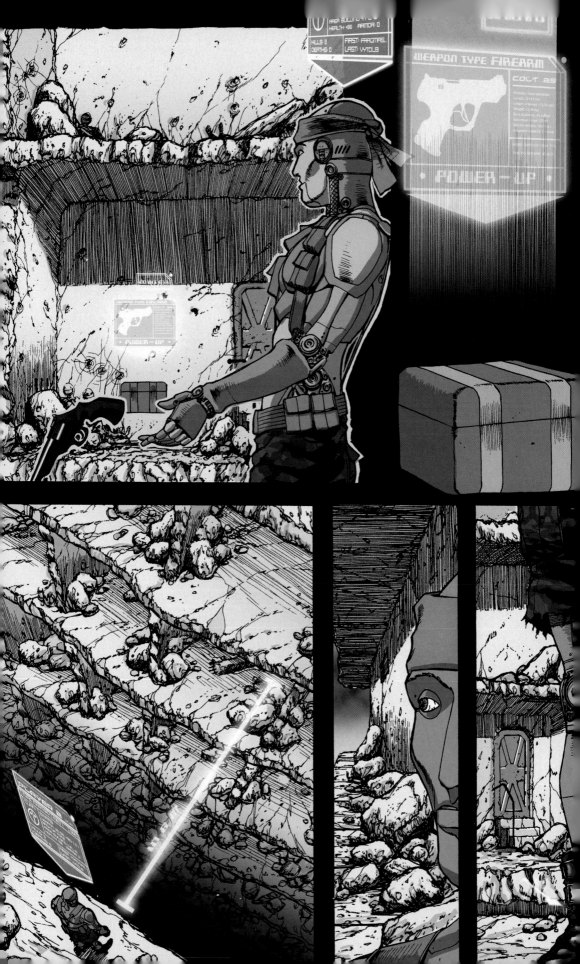

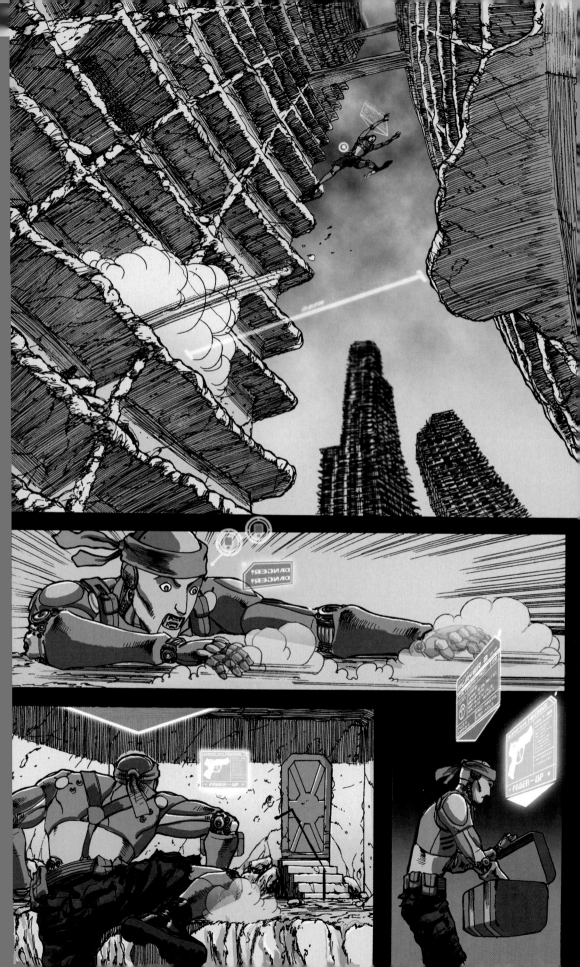

INITIATING AUTO-SCRIPT.....
    LOAD OS P2PRIME v. 6.2.03
    PASS? ********
RUNNNING...

SYSTEM NOW ONLINE.......

AREA: BUILDING 4 FL. 18
HEALTH: +96   ARMOR: 0
KILLS: 3   FIRST: FRAGMAS...
DEATHS: 0   LAST: VYTDUB

CONNECTED

BLAM BLAMBLAMBLAM
BLAM BLAM
BLAM
BLAM

PLAYER 2 WINS
PLAYER 2 LEVELS UP

NEXT LEVEL AT 19000XP

START NEW GAME ? Y
LOADING....
    MAP: THE GAUNTLET

BEGIN MATCH
    3....2....1....

"DO YOU THINK I'M CRAZY?"

BEEP

"YEAH, UH, IT'S ME... ESSIE. I HAVE TO GO OUT, SO I LEFT YOUR STUFF WITH GINA. JUST RING THE BUZZER— SHE KNOWS YOU'RE COMING. I'M SORRY, I-I KNOW YOU'D WANTED TO DO THIS IN PERSON, BUT..."

THE BUTTERFLY CONSERVATORY
Tropical Butterflies Alive in Winter

"...I'VE GOT SOMEWHERE ELSE I NEED TO BE."

Story	Art	Colors	Letters
kelly sue deconnick	andy macdonald	meg hunt	kristyn ferretti

Tropical Butterflies Alive in Winter

The stairs slope here, awkwardly.

Like the building got tired and a hundred years later,
decided to lean on the other foot.

Below it, the trains burrow past with a noise that stirs concrete from here to the Island.

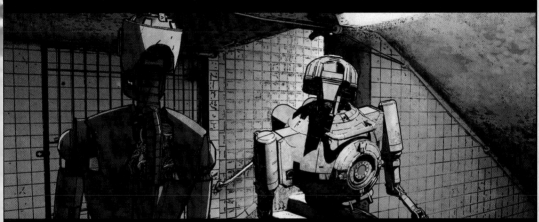

It drowns out her words, but her sneer helps me get the idea.

Vuk smells like the F train, or the F smells like him.

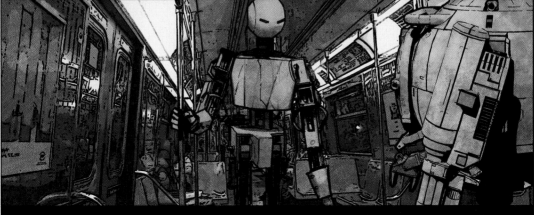

He rattles on, literally. He scrapes and clicks about taxes and death and the end of the world.

This is where I met Mima, reading names off the posters in a whisper that I'd barely hear.

For a month we'd pass at the same time and place until one day she was gone.

This one tells me again that the world's gonna burst into flames.

Then he crosses and gets to work warning the rest of the city.

In the Red Light I'm offered a much better road to Damnation.

She smells like old diesel.
She looks like she means it.

The black market crashes and booms with the clatter of scrap that once moved on its own.

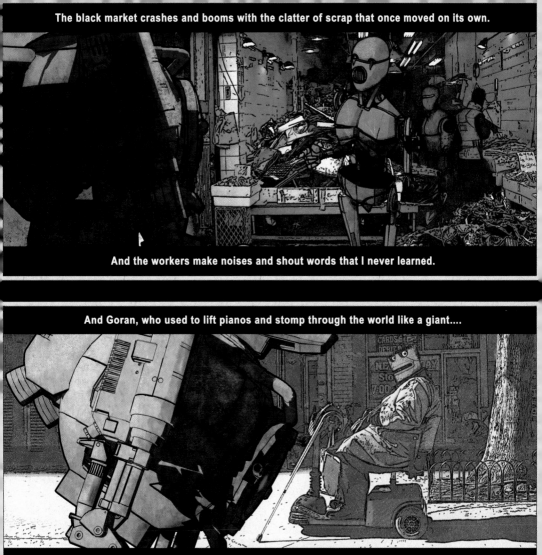

And the workers make noises and shout words that I never learned.

And Goran, who used to lift pianos and stomp through the world like a giant....

Goran whistles at me and goes right back to humming some song.

And the days are shorter now, and the street starts getting dark.

But like the day, only one of us can see it.

All he said was, "nice shirt".

He wasn't smug or condescending.

...about how many hours I had spent at a job I don't like...

And I couldn't stop thinking...

...to buy this,

"nice shirt".

As I started to look-

Wolf Larsen, it was always Wolf Larsen, enslaver and tormentor of men, a male Circe and these his swine, suffering brutes that grovelled before him and revolted only in drunkenness and in secrecy. And was I, too, one of his swine?

-I started to find **time**.

As I pushed-

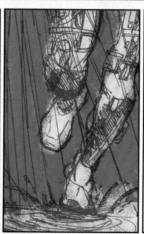

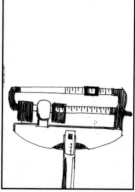

-I found **strength**.

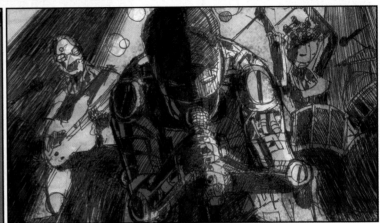

I didn't even vote in 2000.

I guess I took a lot of things for granted.

National March on Washingt
END the WAR on IRAQ
SATURDAY
SEPT 24

Then my brother was killed in Tikrit.

Rob reminds me a lot of my brother.

END

Fear and Self-Loathing in NYC

Jonathan L. Davis
SCRIPT

Tony Moore
ART

Bill Crabtree
COLORS

S.A. Finch
LETTERS

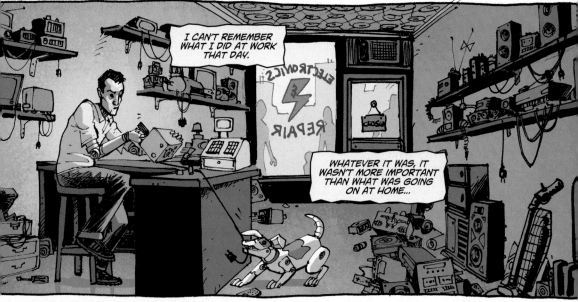

EVERY DAY I LIVE WITH THE GUILT.

I WISH I HAD DIED WITH HER.

GROUP THERAPY ACCIDENTAL DEATH

I KNOW EXACTLY HOW YOU FEEL.

A COUPLE YEARS AGO, MY HUSBAND CLIMBED UP TO MY BEDROOM LIKE HE USED TO DO WHEN WE WERE TEENAGERS.

HE WANTED TO SURPRISE ME FOR MY BIRTHDAY.

I REALIZED TOO LATE WHAT I HAD DONE.

UNFORTUNATELY, I THOUGHT HE WAS A BURGLAR.

AND LIKE YOU, ALL I FEEL IS GUILT AND SHAME. I'M GONNA HAVE THAT FOR THE REST OF MY LIFE

THE FIRST TWO DEATHS WERE AN ACCIDENT. BUT YOU JUMP NOW, KNOWING THAT HE'S JUMPING WITH YOU--

--THAT WON'T BE AN ACCIDENT.

SHIT.

COME ON, CHESTER.

TICKET GETS PAID IN 30 DAYS OR IT DOUBLES.

The End

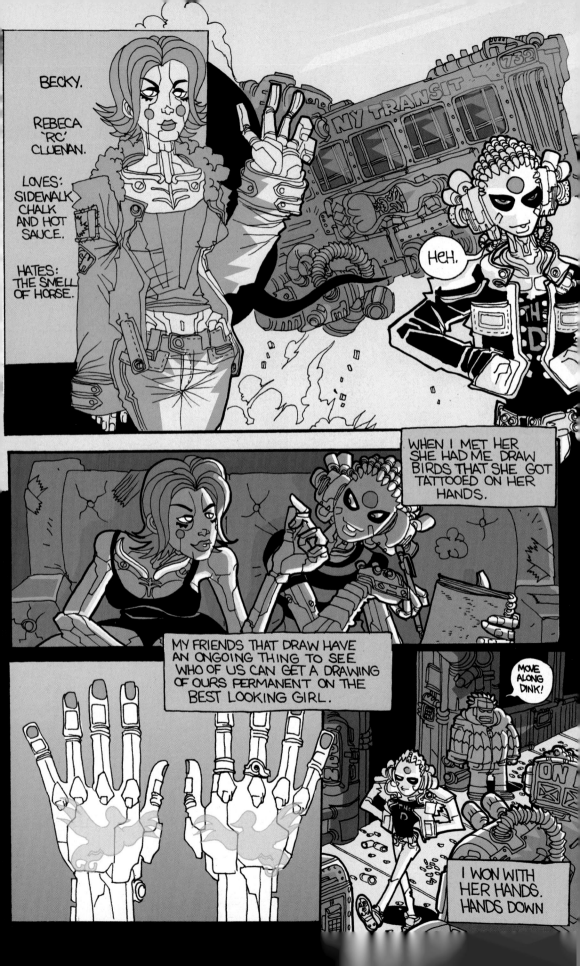

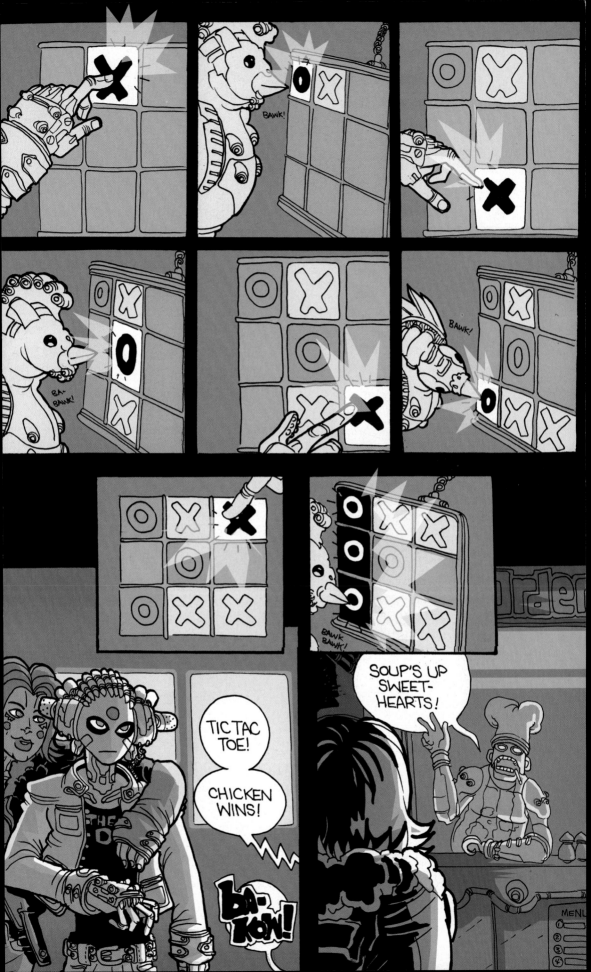

OR MAYBE NOT...

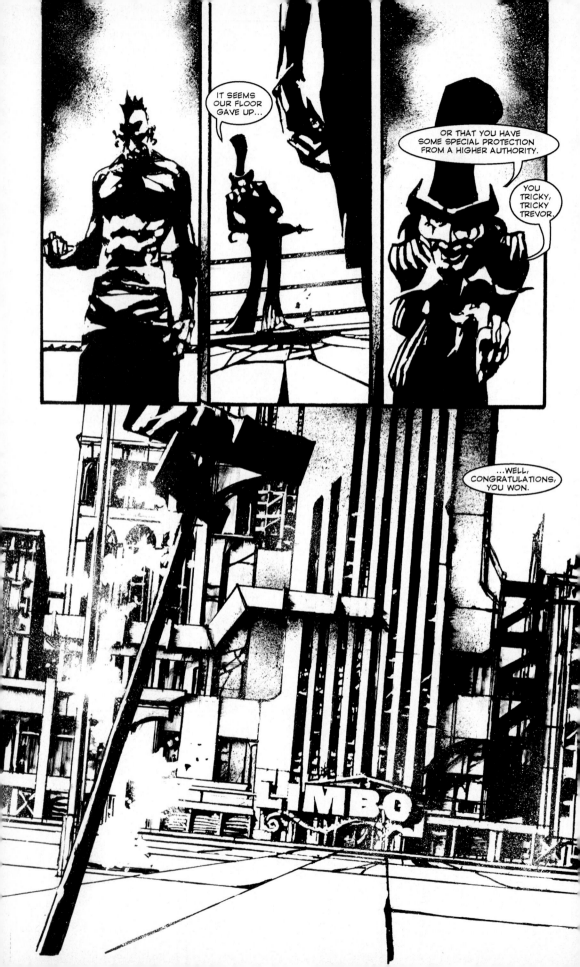

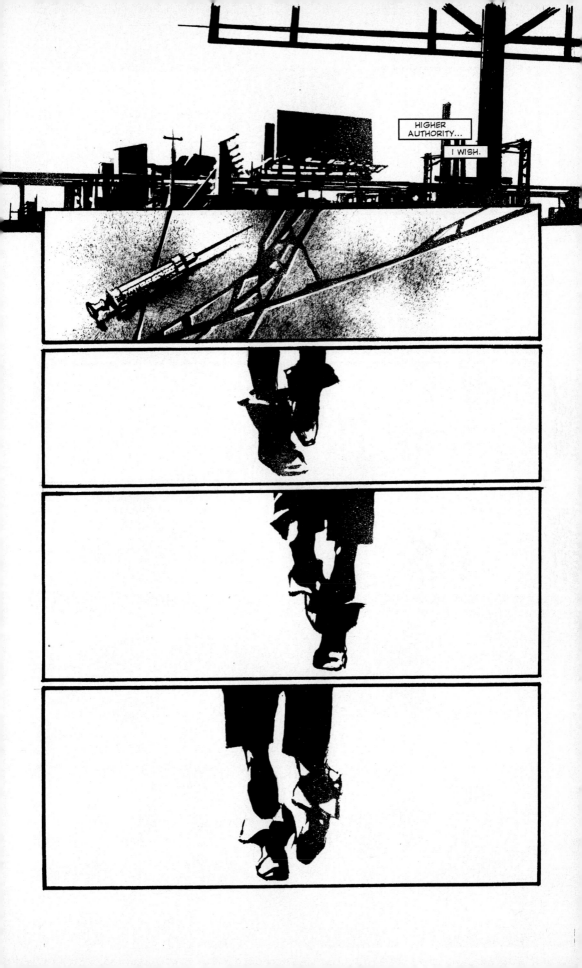

LIKE...
HEAVEN.

YES.

DOESN'T MATTER. ANYWAY, NOBODY ELSE SHOWED UP EITHER.

OH, WHO ELSE DID YOU CALL?

THEM GUYS THAT STAY AT C-SQUAT?

NO, WE DIDN'T CALL ANYBODY, BUT THERE WASN'T *ANYBODY* AT THE SHOW.

EH, I HAVEN'T BEEN TO CBs IN A WHILE...

YOU GUYS SHOULD PLAY AGAIN, HERE.

SHAME, REALLY. WE SOUNDED AMAZING.

I'M IN.

WHERE? IN THIS TINY APARTMENT?

ON THE ROOF!

LET'S DO IT.

ZZZIP

HEY...

...JEFF??

I'M TALKING TO MYSELF HERE, AREN'T I?

tek

clink

FLUSH

story
IVAN BRANDON

art
DAN PANOSIAN

NONE OF THEM KNEW THEY WERE ROBOTS

Benito Cereno: script
Nate Bellegarde: art
Nick Filardi: color
S.A. Finch: letters

"I TELL YOU WHAT, MAN. THIS IS THE HARDEST THING IN THE WORLD."

"YEAH."

I MEAN, IT'S SERIOUSLY HARD. AND TELEVISION AND MOVIES MAKE IT LOOK SO EASY.

YOU PUT TWO PEOPLE OF COMPATIBLE SEXUALITIES TOGETHER, AND IF THEY STAY IN THE SAME ROOM OR HERD SHEEP TOGETHER LONG ENOUGH, THEY WILL EVENTUALLY, THROUGH THE SHEER WILLPOWER OF THE AUDIENCE'S DESIRE TO LIVE THROUGH THEM, START MAKING THE FUCK OUT.

THAT SOUNDS GOOD.

YEAH, IT DOES BUT UNFORTUNATELY IT DOESN'T WORK THAT WAY.

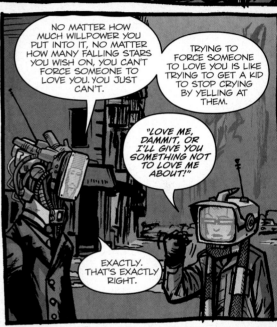

NO MATTER HOW MUCH WILLPOWER YOU PUT INTO IT, NO MATTER HOW MANY FALLING STARS YOU WISH ON, YOU CAN'T FORCE SOMEONE TO LOVE YOU. YOU JUST CAN'T.

TRYING TO FORCE SOMEONE TO LOVE YOU IS LIKE TRYING TO GET A KID TO STOP CRYING BY YELLING AT THEM.

"LOVE ME, DAMMIT, OR I'LL GIVE YOU SOMETHING NOT TO LOVE ME ABOUT!"

EXACTLY. THAT'S EXACTLY RIGHT.

AND AS MUCH AS HOLLYWOOD WOULD LIKE YOU TO BELIEVE OTHERWISE, WOMEN ARE PEOPLE, TOO. SHE'S JUST AS HUMAN AS YOU AND I ARE. AND AS A HUMAN, SHE'S IN CONTROL OF HER OWN DESTINY.

UNFORTUNATELY, AS A WOMAN, SHE'S ALSO IN CHARGE OF YOUR DESTINY AS WELL.

THAT... DOESN'T SOUND VERY PROGRESSIVE. I THOUGHT YOU WERE A FEMINIST.

DON'T GET CONFUSED, BROTHER. MY BRAIN IS A FEMINIST. MY HEART IS A MISOGYNIST.

SUP, NERDS?

WHAT ARE YOU RIM-JAMMERS TALKING ABOUT?

WELL,  WAS JUST TALKING ABOUT HOW YOU LOVE BONERS.

IS THIS TRUE? DO YOU LOVE BONERS?

WELL... YOU GUYS ARE BONERS, AND I LOVE YOU, SO... YES?

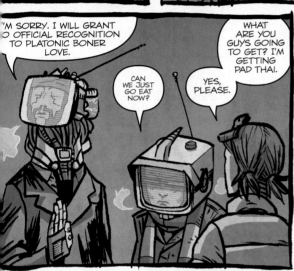

I'M SORRY. I WILL GRANT OFFICIAL RECOGNITION TO PLATONIC BONER LOVE.

CAN WE JUST GO EAT NOW?

YES, PLEASE.

WHAT ARE YOU GUYS GOING TO GET? I'M GETTING PAD THAI.

"I'M GOING TO GET PAD THAI, TOO."

"PAD THAI? YOU GUYS EAT LIKE TOURISTS, MAN."

OH YEAH? WHAT ARE YOU GOING TO ORDER, DOCTOR AWESOME?

I'M GOING TO GET THE ONG BAK SPECIAL.

CONSIDERING THAT I THINK THAT'S AN ELBOW TO THE FACE-- GOOD CHOICE.

WELL, TOM YUM GOONG HAS ELEPHANTS IN IT, AND I REFUSE TO--

TRYING TO FOLLOW A CONVERSATION BETWEEN YOU TWO IS LIKE EAVESDROPPING ON A CHARLIE BROWN PTA MEETING-- WAH WOH WOH WAH WUH.

DUDE, THAT WAS AWESOME!

FIVE BUCKS AWESOME?

YES, FIVE BUCKS AWESOME.

HEY, N, I JUST GAVE THAT GUY MY LAST FIVE BUCKS. CAN YOU PICK UP MY LUNCH?

YES. YES, I CAN.

DUDE, DO YOU THINK THAT WAS IT?

THE MOMENT?

GOD...

GOD, I HOPE NOT.

01100101
01101110
01100100

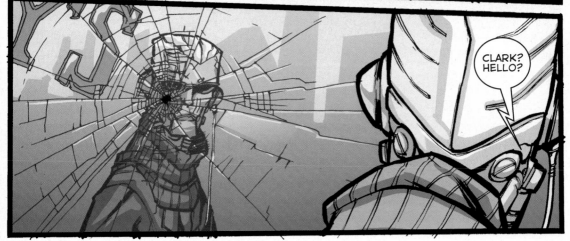

OH MY GOD.

CLARK!!

I'M HERE, I'M...

I JUST GOT...

END

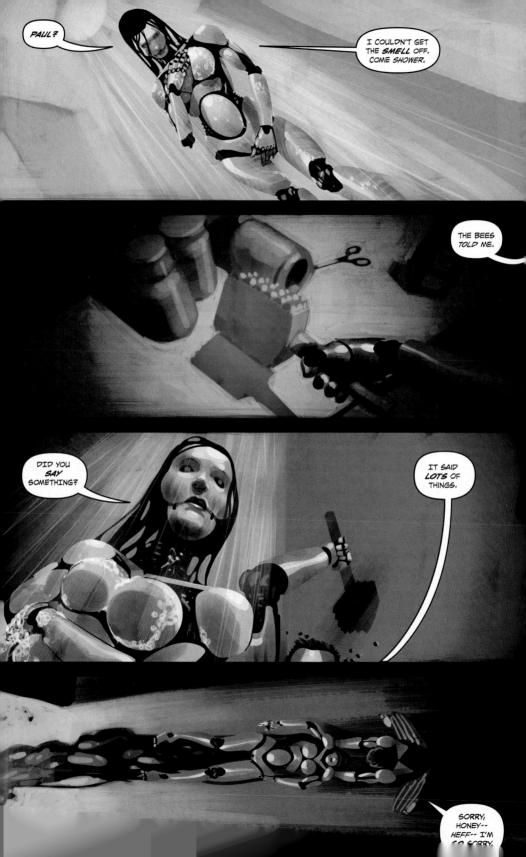

JOSE LUIS ÁGREDA
lives with his wife in a sunny apartment in Seville, where he draws comics and illustrations for the top magazines and publishers in Spain.
http://homepage.mac.com/agreda/iblog

JEFF AMANO
created THE COBBLER'S MONSTER, RED WARRIORS, FADE FROM GRACE, KISS & TELL, and RONIN HOOD. He is the founder of Beckett Comics.

ANJIN
Born in 1972 just outside of Chicago, Anjin attended the University of Illinois as well as The American Academy of Art in Chicago. After a two-year stint designing T-shirts, he leapt into the hectic world of video games and has worked for the last 6 years as a digital artist for Incredible Technologies, Inc. While there he has designed interfaces for video games, mastered 3-D modeling, animation, concept art and recently functioned as lead artist on a 3-year project. When not working on his digital paintings, Anjin freelances in illustration, concept art, graphic design and comic book coloring.

PAUL AZACETA
Born and bred in New Jersey, Paul has wedged his way into the comic community. Having first worked briefly for Marvel comics, he then moved on to Image Comics where he and Mark Sable created a new book called GROUNDED. His main focus now is working on new interesting projects and never losing the ability to stretch himself artistically. He'd like to thank his wonderful wife Austria for her love and support.

FRANK BEATON
is a freelance writer and former contributor to the online comics magazine Ninth Art. He lives in Portland, Oregon, with his wife Jill and several spoiled cats. Neither he nor Jill have ever been to New York City or met a robot in person.

NATE BELLEGARDE
(1984 - ?) stomps about the house snarling and roaring like a Tyrannosaurus Rex when no one is around.

IVAN BRANDON
is the co-creator of NYC MECH, THE CROSS BRONX and the upcoming GIMME DANGER and THE HEAVY. He produced and edited this edition and wrote a lot of it. He desperately needs a vacation.

RYAN BROWN
was born in 1983 in St. Louis Mo. He graduated from the Savannah College of Art and Design in 2005 and now lives in Jersey City where he draws comics and illustrations and tries not to screw up his life too bad.

CHRIS BRUNNER & RICO RENZI
have been jamming together since 2000. Tune in to more of their greatest hits at: www.kickstandkids.com.

ERIC CANETE
is a storyboard artist/designer by day and comic book illustrator by night. His work can be found in animated series such as Aeon Flux, Justice League Unlimited, and the upcoming Superboy and The Legion of Superheroes. His interior comic book work includes WILDCATS: LADYTRON, and CYBERNARY 2.0 and he provided covers for NYC MECH: BETA LOVE. He's lost somewhere in Los Angeles.

BENITO CERENO
writes boring comics for stupid people. He wrote TALES FROM THE BULLY PULPIT and HECTOR PLASM. His favorite beverage is Berry Lemonade Jones Soda.

BECKY CLOONAN
in order to ink this comic, Becky had to evoke her brush with the element of fire.

BILL CRABTREE

in his short career, Bill has lent his palette to SAVAGE DRAGON, INVINCIBLE, MARVEL TEAM UP and a quickly growing list of others. He lives in New Mexico.

DAVID CROSLAND

draws comics, peels shrimp, co-owns a dog, and lives in San Francisco. For more on this kid, go to www.hiredmeat.com and/or www.myspace.com/hiredmeat.

FAREL DALRYMPLE

is currently drawing a book for Marvel called OMEGA THE UNKNOWN. He is also living in Tulsa, avoiding working on his next POP GUN WAR graphic novel for Dark Horse, and trying not to cry himself to sleep every night.

JONATHAN L. DAVIS

has written screenplays for several major studios, including Warner Brothers, Disney, Columbia, and Universal. This is his first foray into comics, unless you count a letter he wrote to SPAWN while in college.

KELLY SUE DECONNICK

can be found on the web at: www.kellysue.com

RAMI EFAL

is an Israeli artist residing in Brooklyn. He has contributed art to films, TV animation, magazines and comics publications and featured at select galleries in NYC. www.ramiefal.com

KRISTYN FERRETTI

is an art director and graphic designer for film and multi-media at a firm in NYC. In her spare moments you can find her lettering and designing books like this one.

NICK FILARDI

grew up in New London, CT listening to Small Town Hero, watching Batman the Animated Series and fending off ladies. After graduating from Savannah College of Art and Design in 2003, he colored for Zylonol Studios under Lee Loughridge in Savannah, GA while maintaining the pretense of working an "office" job. Currently living in South Philly with his three-legged dog, Deniro, he is the colorist for NYC MECH, GROUNDED, DOLL & CREATURE and GØDLAND.

S. A. FINCH

is a graphic designer from Newcastle, UK. His hobbies include monkeys, brunettes, and stealing office supplies (don't lend him your pen). Following a nasty incident involving all three, he accepted lettering into his heart and is now much happier, thank you very much.

MATT FRACTION

lives in Kansas City, MO.

JOHN G

makes comics, zines, flyers, and noise in Cleveland, Ohio. www.ninepanelgrid.com

ROB G

is the artist and co-creator for DEAD WEST, TEENAGERS FROM MARS, and THE COURIERS. He lives in Brooklyn, New York with his wife and bunny.

BRANDON GRAHAM

has spent his life in the comic book trenches. He keeps a grenade in his boot, a shiv near his heart, and plans to go out in a supernova of fury the day his drawing hand stops working. Until then, he digs for nerd gold and sweats Rooster sauce. In the past Brandon has worked for Heavy metal, DC comics, Spumco, NBM. These days he has fallen in with the wrong crowd, the northwest comix union YOSH, he is currently working on his grape flavored, limo-bombing magnumopus KING CITY for Tokyo Pop.

MILES GUNTER

uses Sunn amps, Sabbath riffs and Holmes ionizers to achieve maximum results. His first original graphic novel ZOMBEE will be released October 2006 from Image Comics.

PHIL HESTER

has been writing and drawing comic books for twenty years. His work has been published in over 300 comics such as GREEN ARROW, NIGHTWING, SWAMP THING, OVERSIGHT, ANTOINE SHARPE: THE ATHEIST, THE WRETCH and the upcoming ANT-MAN. He previously collaborated with Mr. Huddleston to produce THE COFFIN and DEEP SLEEPER. They are just beginning their newest book- DEATHLESS. He was once nominated for an Eisner award. Really. He lives in Iowa with his sainted wife and two overachieving kids.

DAN HIPP

is the co-creator/artist of THE AMAZING JOY BUZZARDS, and is working on his new monster, GYAKUSHU! while sometimes missing the monsters he used to teach. www.mrhipp.com

MATT HOLLINGSWORTH

attended the Kubert School straight out of high school, graduated in 1991 and has been working in comics as a color artist ever since. After many nominations, he finally won the Eisner in 1997. In 2004 he made the transition to working on digital visual effects for film on Sky Captain at Stan Winston Digital. Since then he's worked on 6 other films including The Lion, The Witch and the Wardrobe, Fantastic Four and his current gig on Surf's Up, a CG feature at Sony Pictures Imageworks. In comics he is perhaps most known for having worked on HELLBOY, PREACHER and DAREDEVIL. His current comics gig is THE ETERNALS, with Neil Gaiman and John Romita Jr. at Marvel. He drinks a lot of beer.

MIKE HUDDLESTON

An award winning illustrator, Mike has worked for every comic book company he can think of and a few companies that make other stuff. He has co-created a few comics with his friend Phil Hester and they even sold one of those to Hollywood. When not painting comic book covers or hastily drawing and inking some superhero's adventures,

Mike can be found sleeping, eating cookies, or watching The X-Files. He has yet to get a website, so to contact him please visit www.myspace.com/mikehuddleston

ADAM HUGHES

Born, New Jersey, 1967! Escaped, 1993! Currently sipping Mint Juleps "in Jawjuh, awn th' pawch" Occupation: artist! Wanted to be an astronaut, but is afraid of heights.

RIAN HUGHES

This award-winning graphic designer, comic artist and typographer has produced designs for watches, CDs, animated films and Hawaiian shirts for clients from Tokyo to New York. He has a cabinet of Thunderbirds memorabilia, a fridge full of vodka, and a stack of easy listening albums which he plays very quietly. devicefonts.co.uk

MEG HUNT

is an illustrator hiding out in the desert. She enjoys getting her hands dirty with silkscreening and drawing up a storm. When she's not devising cunning plans and diabolical plots, she is typically thinking about potential artwork, videogames, and puppies. (Not necessarily in that order.) You can view her work at www.meghunt.com

FRAZER IRVING

was born in Essex, weaned on comics, and suffers from freelancer's disease (symptoms include being unable to say "no"). He has a voracious appetite for art, music and sex. He has drawn comics for Dark Horse, DC Comics, Marvel comics, 2000AD, Image Comics and much other stuff, and likes to eat curry.

TODD KLEIN

has been lettering comics since 1977. He has won numerous Eisner, Harvey and CBG Fan awards for his work on such projects as Neil Gaiman's SANDMAN and Alan Moore's AMERICA'S BEST COMICS line. He lives in rural southern New Jersey with his wife Ellen and a variety of animals.

PAUL LAU JR.

Why the hell is this guy still alive? Due to his small stature, weak chinese genetics, and testicles so small as to be futile, he should've died years ago. But alas, artistic talent and a quick wit have allowed this man to not only survive but flourish. If you define flourishing as a poor artist who sniffs glue for a quick thrill. From humble beginnings as a Pasadena male crack-whore to a Beverly Hills high priced escort, he now bums around the state of Washington drawing panda bears being sodomized by octopi.

JASEN LEX

has created two comic book series so far, THE GYPSY LOUNGE and THE SCIENCE FAIR. Information about these books can be found at www.awefulbooks.com.

SONNY LIEW

is currently holed away on the island of Singapore thinking up new MALINKY ROBOT stories and working on a comic for Slave Labor Graphics and Disney.

VASILIS LOLOS

was doing comics professionally in Athens Greece for five years. Now he takes on the US. He also like his kafe with cigarettes.

ANDY MACDONALD

Scorpio – Scotch Drinker – Hates loudmouth jerkoffs at parties – Loves kicking the asses of loudmouth jerkoffs at parties – Enjoys drawing robots and has done so for the past couple of years in the Image Comics series NYC MECH– All from a little apartment in Brooklyn, NY.

MICHELLE MADSEN

started her career in the in-house coloring department at Dark Horse Comics, leading her to a freelance career a few years later. Current projects are 13TH SON, LAST CHRISTMAS, CONAN: BOOK OF THOTH, and CITY OF TOMORROW. Michelle resides in Portland, Oregon with her husband Dave and dog Spike.

JIM MAHFOOD

has somehow managed to make a living off his doodles and scribblings since 1997, amassing a huge cult following all over the globe. His work has appeared in comic books, magazines, music videos, ads, animation, on t-shirts, albums, flyers, buttons and various other media.

ALEX MALEEV

Born in 1971 in Sofia, Bulgaria, Alex studied at the Academy of Fine Arts before moving to NYC in 1994. In comics, his credits include: HELLBOY WEIRD TALES, DAREDEVIL, and ILLUMINATI, his film credits include The Bone Collector and Great Expectations He was the industry's Russ Manning Award winner in 1996 and won an Eisner for his work on DAREDEVIL.

PROCEEDS FOR ALEX'S WORK
IN THIS EDITION WILL BE
DONATED TO A.C.T.O.R.

PAUL MAYBURY

rules over the Boston comics scene with an Iron Fist. He also hates shaking hands at conventions, specifically YOUR hand. If you come across him, do not make eye contact. a simple bow of respect will suffice. Visit www.deliciousbrains.com

DAVE MCCAIG

is a veteran of comics and animation. In 2003 he founded GUTTERZOMBIE, one of the industry's foremost resources for upcoming and professional colorists. He lives in Vancouver and enjoys eating brains.

FÁBIO MOON AND GABRIEL BÁ

These twin brothers from Brazil share lots of things in life, including their unstoppable passion for comics. Fábio caught the attention of the American public with his fluid and expressive art in SMOKE AND GUNS in 2005 and Gabriel is about to catch everyone by surprise with his inspired work on CASANOVA. After a great start doing the art on the Xeric Grant winner ROLAND, DAYS OF WRATH, published by Terra Major in 1999, they had a story in AUTOBIOGRAPHIX in 2003, their modern fairy tale URSULA was published in 2004 and in 2005, Image Comics published their experimental comic ROCK'N'ROLL. Their award winning work has been translated to English, Spanish and Italian. De:TALES, a collection of their stories, is to be published by Dark Horse. fabioandgabriel.blogspot.com

TONY MOORE
is a small-town guy from Kentucky, raised by a pack of wild televisions. He's been in the business since 1999, when he started work on his maiden voyage, BATTLE POPE. Since then he's lent his hand to drawing FEAR AGENT and THE EXTERMINATORS and was nominated for an eisner for his work on THE WALKING DEAD.

MICHAEL AVON OEMING
lives in New Jersey and is trying to get out when he is not writing for Marvel, RED SONJA or drawing POWERS.

DAN PANOSIAN
has been helplessly hypnotized by the self described "splendor" that is Ivan Brandon. In a desperate act of obsequious flattery he completed the art for Flush in hopes that Ivan will release his twisted hold over him. His cave scratchings can be viewed at: www.danpanosian.com

LELAND PURVIS
writes and draws comics with antique tools and animal hair on cotton paper using graphite, and ink made of blackened sap from the tree of life. He loves, labors, thinks and drinks in Brooklyn, NY.

RICK REMENDER
Rick's accomplishments include producing numerous creator-owned comics including STRANGE GIRL, BLACK HEART BILLY, FEAR AGENT, SEA OF RED, NIGHT MARY and DOLL AND CREATURE. Rick is married to Danni Remender who is British and better than him. They have cats and live in the Bay Area of Northern California.

ESAD RIBIC
started drawing comics for underground strips in grade school. He has since worked for Antarctic Press, Marvel and DC Vertigo. He plays drums, drinks espresso and smokes a lot of cigarettes. He lives in Zagreb, Croatia and knows where to find all the best mine fields.

JOHN NEY RIEBER
has been writing comics long enough to know better. But his love of the medium and the collaborative aspects of graphic storytelling continue to assert precedence over his grasp of reality.

EDUARDO RISSO
did his first professional work for the daily paper La Nacion and the magazines Eroticon and Satiricon . In 1997, he teamed up with Brian Azzarello on the miniseries JONNY DOUBLE which led to the creation of the multiple Eisner Award winning series 100 BULLETS, which has earned him both Eisner and Harvey awards for best artist.

CLEM ROBINS
has been lettering comics since 1977. His work has been twice nominated for the Harvey awards and once for the Wizard awards. His current projects include 100 BULLETS, LOVELESS, HELLBOY, B.P.R.D., and Y: THE LAST MAN. His book THE ART OF FIGURE DRAWING was published in 2002 by North Light Books, and still makes the ideal gift for any occasion. He teaches figure drawing and human anatomy at the Art Academy of Cincinnati. His pictures are in collections all over the country, and in the permanent collection of the Cincinnati Art Museum. Robins lives in Norwood, Ohio with his very lovely and very patient wife Lisa.

JIM RUGG
is the co-creator of STREET ANGEL, AFRODISIAC, and THE PLAIN JANES. His comics have appeared in a slew of anthologies, including PROJECT: SUPERIOR, PROJECT: ROMANTIC, TRUEPORN, TYPEWRITER, SPX, MEATHAUS, and ORCHID 2.

NEAL SHAFFER
is a writer from Baltimore, MD. His previous work includes the Oni Press comic books LAST EXIT BEFORE TOLL, ONE PLUS ONE, and BORROWED TIME.

KELSEY SHANNON
has worked in animation and film and is the artist and co-creator of Bastard Samurai. He lives in Texas.

LAKOTA SIOUX
is a New York based, self taught artist, who's original written and illustrated story CAMPUS MEATS can be seen in NBM publishing's erotic quarterly , 'Sizzle' magazine. Sioux's currently the cover artist for the horror comic HALF DEAD and does various freelance for Independent music labels as an album cover and CD interior designer.

MARK ANDREW SMITH
is the writer and co-creator of THE AMAZING JOY BUZZARDS at Image Comics. His current project is AQUA THE CONQUEROR with Paul Maybury.

RICK SPEARS
is a writer of comic books and a publisher of Gigantic Graphic Novels. His hit list includes TEENAGERS FROM MARS, DEAD WEST, FILLER and coming soon THE PIRATES OF CONEY ISLAND, REPO and BLACK METAL. www.giganticgraphicnovels.com

DAVE STEWART
started his career in comics as a design intern at Dark Horse, worked his way into the coloring department and a few years later went freelance. Current awards include two Harveys and two Eisners. Current and upcoming projects include: HELLBOY, BPRD, CONAN, SUPERMAN, BATMAN, and WINTERMEN. Dave resides in Portland, Oregon with his wife Michelle and dog Spike.

JAMES STOKOE
has a removable tooth full of cyanide reserved for the second the goons try to take him alive. He's made a blood oath promise to mountaintop Norse Viking gods to draw comics chocked full of monster destruction, cocks and boomerangs. He is part of the northwest's comic book frontline, YOSH! His next book is a space trucker chef epic from Oni press: WONTON SOUP.

BEN TEMPLESMITH
likes Sumo Wrestling and can hold more alcohol than you in all probability as he is Australian. These days Ben lives and works on things like FELL with Warren Ellis and WORMWOOD: GENTLEMAN CORPSE which he writes and draws himself, in his studio in Perth where he attempts in vain to get what those in the 'industry' call 'sleep' at least a couple hours a day. There's also a strange American lurking about his home, although she could easily be a figment of a caffeine-induced delirium.

FRANK TERAN
Jersey's own mutated art abomination... this wise-cracking pol-uban swaggler of the comics and gaming industry epitomizes the word obscurity. He spends his days in the lab...secluded...cooking up lowbrow visuals... and skanky narrative antics. He also thinks bios are very creepy...3rd person epitaphs... so he'll wrap this up and thank his wife, family and friends for tolerating his neurotic shenanigans.

GREG THOMPSON
is the writer and co-creator of HERO CAMP and ATOMIC CHIMP, and the deputy director of CBLDF. He lives with his wife and two cats in Brooklyn, NY

DANIJEL ZEZELJ
is the author of more than twenty graphic novels. His work has been exhibited throughout Europe and the US, and his illustrations and comics have been published by, among others, DC Comics/Vertigo, Marvel Comics, The New York Times Book Review, Harper's Magazine and Image Comics.

Cover by ADAM HUGHES

Produced and Edited by
IVAN BRANDON

Art Direction and Book Design by
KRISTYN FERRETTI

Supplemental Book Art by
ANDY MACDONALD, FRANK TERAN
AND ADAM HUGHES

Our Thanks To Every One
Of The Amazing Contributors
To This Volume Of 24seven.

Special Thanks To
Kristyn Ferretti, Nick Filardi,
Adam Hughes, Allison Sohn, Eric
Stephenson, Jim Demonakos,
Erik Larsen, Allen Hui, Laurenn
McCubbin, Mike Hawthorne, Jim
Rugg and The City of New York.

All Characters Are Purely Fictional. Any
Relation To Humans Or Robots, Living
Or Dead, Is Purely Coincidental.

No Robots Were Harmed During
The Making Of 24seven.

If You Enjoyed This Book,
We Encourage You To Pick Up
NYC MECH: LET'S ELECTRIFY &
NYC MECH: BETA LOVE
www.nycmech.com

IMAGE COMICS, INC.
Erik Larsen - Publisher
Todd McFarlane - President
Marc Silvestri - CEO
Jim Valentino - Vice-President

Eric Stephenson - Executive Director
Jim Demonakos - PR & Marketing Coordinator
Mia MacHatton - Accounts Manager
Traci Hui - Administrative Assistant
Joe Keatinge - Traffic Manager
Allen Hui - Production Manager
Jonathan Chan - Production Artist
Drew Gill - Production Artist
www.imagecomics.com